WAN
DARK... R

BY
JANE A C WEST

ILLUSTRATED BY
ANTHONY WILLIAMS

MY LIFE

FULL FLIGHT

Titles in the Full Flight Heroes and Heroines series:

Badger Publishing Limited
Oldmedow Road, Hardwick Industrial Estate,
King's Lynn PE30 4JJ
Telephone: 01438 791037
www.badgerlearning.co.uk

2 4 6 8 10 9 7 5 3 1

Wanda Darkstar ISBN 978-1-84926-468-6

First edition © 2011
This second edition © 2014

Text © Jane A C West 2011
Complete work © Badger Publishing Limited 2011

Badger Publishing would like to thank Jonny Zucker for his help
in putting this series together.

Publisher: David Jamieson
Senior Editor: Danny Pearson
Design: Fiona Grant
Illustration: Anthony Williams

Contents

Badger
LEARNING

New words:

Tentacles - arm/leg of an octopus or squid

Quarantine - where animals/people are isolated from others

Disguise - clothing/mask to change or hide the way you look

Main characters:

Wanda Darkstar - Alien Welfare Officer

Rex Squid - an alien

Dr Hubble - a government scientist

Chapter 1

How to look like a Human

Most days my life is pretty easy.
But every now and then it isn't.
Today was one of those days.

For one thing my rocketship was in the
garage for repairs. And for another, it
was still only Tuesday.

Yes, I have a rocketship - which is
pretty cool - but I need it for my job.

It might come as a shock to you but
Earth isn't as alone as most humans
imagine.

Lots of aliens live here happily.

I should know - I'm one of them.
But apart from me, you get a lot of
Venusians (who want to live in a cooler
climate);

a lot of Plutonians
(who are looking
for a warmer one);

and a lot of Martians
(who like having a
free bus pass for the
over 60s).

My job is to make sure that all these aliens live happily alongside humans - and don't get found out.

The number one rule is to never, ever, ever tell humans that aliens exist.

So I spend a lot of my time with the newest arrivals giving lessons in basic human behaviour. Stuff like: watch football, don't snack on litter or cat food, don't chase sticks in the park, and always hide your tentacles.

Pretty basic really, but mostly they catch on fast. Mostly.

Rex Squid was the exception. He didn't want to hide his tentacles and he didn't see why humans shouldn't know about him.

"Because it's the law, Rex," I said.

"X~u*edfd!98u@we4r#d," he said. Which translated as, "These clothes are really cramped. I like to feel the grass under my tentacles when I slither in the park."

"You can't Rex," I said, as patiently as I could. "Humans would be totally freaked out if they saw what you really looked like. When you got your passport for Earth, you agreed that you'd keep your real self hidden. As I said, it's the law."

Well, he didn't like that and wanted to argue a bit more but I couldn't make an exception for him.

Eventually he left, grumbling to himself.

I thought that was that - but I was wrong.

Chapter 2

A Bad Feeling

I got my job in Alien Welfare (Solar System, Sector 1247) because I have a nose for trouble. It's like a sixth sense, although the other five come in handy, too.

I had an uneasy feeling so I decided to check out the alien forums and chat-rooms.

Something definitely wasn't right - they were all too happy. Aliens, like most humans, enjoy a good grumble: this lot were... chirpy. It wasn't normal. And it made me nervous.

It was when I ran the location scan
programme that I knew it was going to
be a bad day.

"Uh oh! Rex Squid has left quarantine!"

It takes some aliens quite a long time to
get used to being on Earth - different
gravity and all that. Modifying their
behaviour can be tricky, too. I had one
family of Lunar mice who kept scaring
the local cats. That had to stop - people
were starting to notice.

Anyway, aliens are kept in quarantine until they're ready to mix properly with humans. It's not like prison or anything - they just all have to stay in one town until they're ready. Is it your town? I'll leave it to you to guess.

Now Rex Squid was on his way to the bus station. I had to get there - fast.

That's when I remembered that my rocketship was lying in pieces in some chop shop on Mars.

I had to think quickly.

Hoverboard: no license for use on Earth.

Anti-gravity boots: stand out too much.

I didn't have a whole lot of choice -
it would have to be the scooter.

Chapter 3

Squid Escape

It didn't take me long to realise that Rex wasn't travelling in disguise.

"Did you see that?"
A nervous looking woman was gripping her toddler's hand.

"W-what was that?" she said.

"That's my uncle," I said. "Brilliant fancy dress costume, isn't it?"

"Oh, yes," she said faintly. "How does he do the slime trail?"

Rex had come out of hiding - which meant his tentacles were showing. I had to move - fast.

Rex had got as far as the chip shop when I caught sight of him.

He was handing out leaflets to advertise his new autobiography, 'My Life on Earth'. He'd even autographed them!

I realised he'd been planning this for a long time.

"I don't understand," said a man in a puzzled voice. "Is this some sort of joke?"

"Yeah, it's to advertise that new science fiction film," I said.

"Oh, is that all?" and he tossed the flyer in a bin.

"One down, 99 to go," I said.

Luckily, most people don't read flyers they are given in the street - they just take them politely and bin them later.

But one grey-haired man was reading the flyer intently. I'd have to get that flyer off him later.

I realised I'd been distracted.

I looked around me urgently, but it was too late - the Squid had gone.

Chapter 4

Bus Station Banter

I caught up with Rex standing in the centre of the bus station. There was quite a crowd.

Rex definitely wasn't going to make it easy for me. He knew I couldn't zap him in full view of humans. I had to get him by himself - and Rex wasn't going to let that happen.

Rex was checking out the timetable - it looked like he was planning to head for London.

Not on my watch.

Suddenly Rex turned round and slithered straight towards me.

"What do you want, Darkstar?" he said.

"You know I can't let you do this, Rex," I replied. "You've got to come with me."

"No way! I am sick of acting like a human. I want everyone on Earth to see the real me."

"It's not going to happen, Rex. Don't make me zap you."

I don't like to threaten my aliens -
I prefer to just talk to them.
But sometimes, just sometimes, I have
to zap them.

This means that they have to spend the
rest of their lives frozen into human
shape.

Rex looked worried.
"You wouldn't!" he gulped.

"Only as a last resort, Rex. But you're
not making this easy."

Then he grinned, showing a couple of
fangs.

"You wouldn't dare zap me in public," he snorted.

He was right. I hate it when that happens. And anyway, I didn't tell Rex, but the zap-ray wasn't working properly. I didn't know what it would do.

Just then a woman tapped me on the shoulder.
"I can recommend a good dentist for your poor friend," she said, pointing at Rex.

I smiled thinly. "It's just a costume for a film he's making."

"Oh! It looks so real," she replied.

Why are humans so observant just when you want them to look the other way?

And then the grey-haired man with the flyer turned up.

Chapter 5

Rex's Mistake

"I am Dr Hubble," said the grey-haired man. "I am a scientist for the government. I'd like to talk to you about your flyer... and... er... tentacles."

"It's a cool costume, isn't it?" I said desperately.

"It's no costume!" snorted Rex.

"I'm interested in what you say about the gravity on Mars. How did you get this information? We've only just found it out using our remote scanner.
How could you possibly know?"

Rex smiled and the man took a step back.

I had to take control of the situation.
"Uncle, Rex! I feel sick!"

I grabbed hold of Rex's arm.

"What?"

"Your niece does look a little nauseous..."

"Yes, yes! I'm going to be sick!"

I may be small, but I'm stronger than I look. I managed to drag Rex away.

It's easier to drag someone with tentacles than someone with feet.

"Listen, Darkstar," said Rex. "One day humans will have to know the truth - why not today?"

"No way, Rex. They're not ready."

"But don't you wonder, Wanda, what it would be like?" he said nastily. "We could rule this planet."

Rex had gone too far. He knew it - I knew it.

He saw the look on my face.

"D-don't zap me!" he snivelled.

But I had no choice.

"Sorry, Rex. I have to make sure you're safe for humans."

And then I zapped him.

But something was wrong! The zap-ray was supposed to freeze him in his human form, but Rex was shrinking!

Suddenly I realised what was wrong: Rex had been frozen in human form - but the age of a child not an adult.

"Sorry, Rex," I said. "I think you'll be going back to school - for a very long time."

Rex was furious: he looked like a kid having a tantrum - which he was.

When I'd arranged for him to be fostered with the family of Lunar mice, I got back on my scooter and sailed out of the bus station.

Behind me, the grey-haired man was scratching his head, still looking very confused.

Darkstar Confidential

Our Solar System

'Solar' is the Greek word for 'sun'.
The Solar System is made up of all the planets that orbit our Sun.

As well as the planets, the Solar System is made up of moons, comets, asteroids, minor planets, and dust and gas.

The Moon

The Moon is the only place in our Solar System (other than Earth) where people have walked. The first moon walk took place in 1969.

Gravity

Why do apples fall to the ground when they drop from a tree? Why don't they go upwards? The answer is gravity. Without it, that apple would float off into space.

A large, heavy object like the Earth has quite a lot of gravity. The moon has less gravity because it's smaller. If you watch the 'First Moon Landing 1969' on the internet, you'll see that the astronauts walk like they're on a bouncy castle.

The real Darkstar

Although you might not find the name 'Darkstar' in your local telephone book, they are real. A darkstar is a term used in astronomy (the study of stars). A darkstar has such a strong gravitational pull that it can trap light.

Questions

- *How many forms of transport does Wanda have?*

- *How many different species of aliens does Wanda mention?*

- *How does Wanda find Rex?*

- *Why does Rex want to reveal himself?*

- *What does Wanda's zap-ray do?*

- *What goes wrong?*

- *Why will Rex have to go to school "for a very long time?"*